The S ng of the DO

Also by Hilda Offen

Blue Balloons and Rabbit Ears

Message from the Moon

HILDA OFFEN

For Belle

Published by TROIKA
First published 2018
1 3 5 7 9 10 8 6 4 2

A CIP catalogue record for this book is available from the British Library
ISBN 978-1-909991-75-0
Printed in Poland

Troika Books Ltd
Well House, Green Lane, Ardleigh CO7 7PD, UK
www.troikabooks.com

Contents

Never!

That Was Then

This is Now

Cloudland

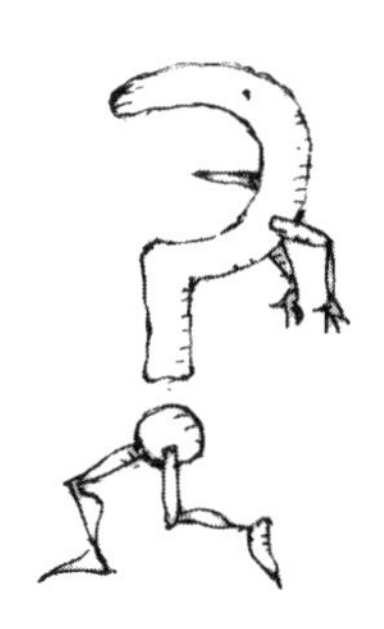

Never!

Oh Yeah?

My mum's bigger
Than yours – so there!
She can wrestle a lion
Or a polar bear.
She can turn you to stone
With a single glance –
And she's swum the Channel
From here to France.

Well – mine's got muscles
Like you've never seen.
She's moody and fierce
And incredibly mean.
She eats rocks for her tea
And spreads nails on her bread;
She can balance a hippo
On top of her head.

Grandad's Nest

When my grandad came home from the sea
He retired to a nest in a tree.
He was joined by a hen,
Two brown bears and a wren,
A goat and a small chimpanzee.

Light as a Feather

She weighs nothing, does my Auntie Heather;
I'm not kidding – she's light as a feather.
In fact, she's so light
That she soars like a kite
When she's out in the wind and the weather.

Geraldine MacAleen!
See her on the trampoline!
Boing! Boing! Boing!

Geraldine! She's the queen!
The bouncy queen of the trampoline!
Boing! Boing! Boing!

You've never seen anyone
Bounce so high –
She's just turned a somersault
Into the sky!
Boing!

She zoomed up like a rocket –
A lightning streak!
We're expecting her down
Any time next week.

Scaredy-cat

My brother says I'm a scaredy-cat –
I'm scared of this and I'm scared of that.

He says there's nothing I don't find frightening –
I'm scared of thunder and I'm scared of lightning.

I'm scared of dragons, I'm scared of sharks –
I'm scared of ghosts and I'm scared of the dark.

I'm scared of volcanoes and vampire bats
And I'm scared of yetis and giant black rats.

He might be right – it might be true –
But be careful, Jim – I know about you!

Last night in the bathroom
I heard you yelp –
"Quick, Mum! It's a spider!
Help, Mum! Help!"

Pantomime Horse

So – your dad tells bad jokes
And your mum sings off-key.
What makes you suppose
That you're worse off than me?

My mum and my dad
Are a pantomime horse.
So how do I feel? Well –
Embarrassed, of course.

They're much in demand
For receptions and fetes –
Their diary is crammed
With engagements and dates.

Last week, they were asked
To come into school.
They cantered and whinnied -
I felt such a fool.

"Mr Jones!" said my teacher.
"And Mrs Jones too!
Thank you so much for coming –
We love what you do!"

She patted my head and said
"So – here's your foal!"
And I wished that the earth
Could swallow me whole.

See! I'm worse off than you!
Life's tragic, of course,
When you are the child
Of a pantomime horse.

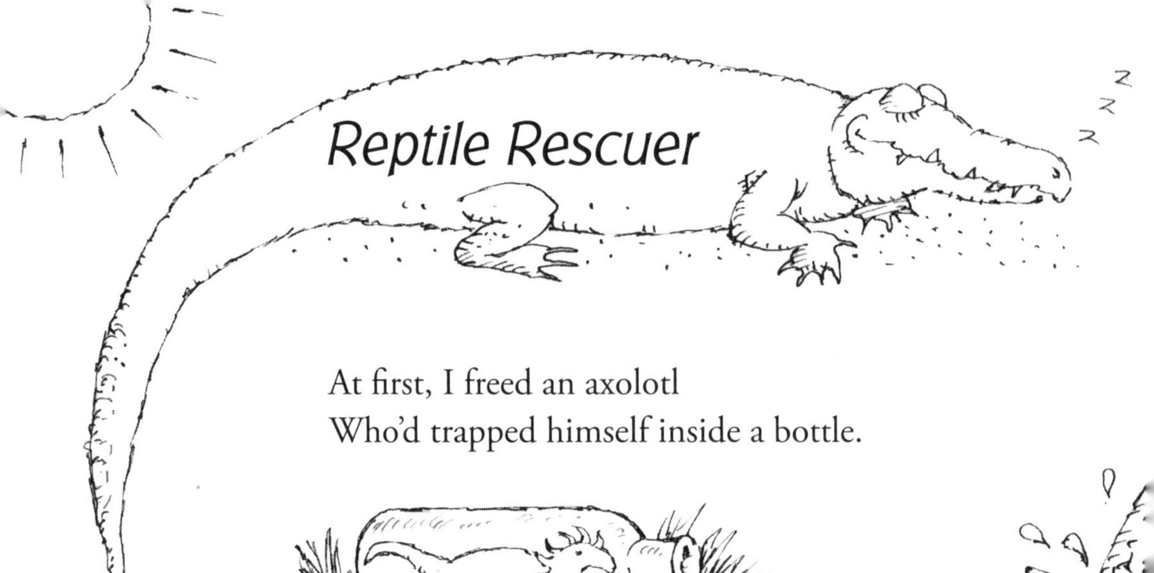

Reptile Rescuer

At first, I freed an axolotl
Who'd trapped himself inside a bottle.

I followed this with rattle-snakes;
I treated them for tummy-aches.

Next came an ailing terrapin –
I dosed him up with aspirin.

And then I straightened out a skink
Whose tail was suffering from a kink .

My last call was a crocodile
Who'd caught the sun upon the Nile.
He seemed asleep – lost in a dream;
I smothered him with suntan cream.

His eyes snapped open. "That's enough!
How dare you coat me with that stuff?"
He glared; and then, without a pause,
He levered wide his gleaming jaws.

That's when I ran – I'd had a scare!
I'll pick my patients with more care.
I won't make any more mistakes –
I'll stick to tortoises and snakes.

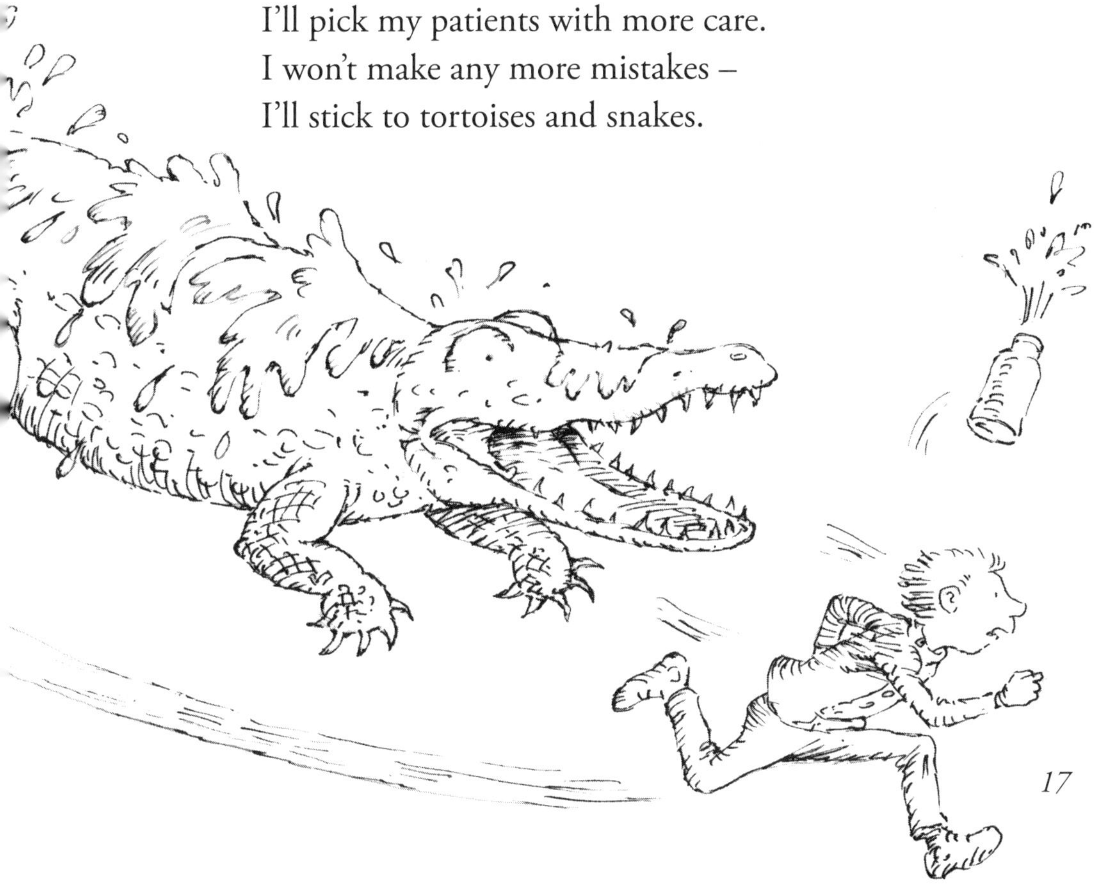

Ears

Charlie's ears are like delicate shells –
They're smaller than Ella's or Isabelle's.
Rover has ears that are soft and flappy;
They wag up and down when he's feeling happy.
And no-one has sticky-out ears like Stu –
They glow rosy-red when the sun shines through.
Aunt Elena's ears are trim and elegant –
But Grandad Bill has ears like an elephant!
Ears like an elephant! Ears like an elephant!
Grandad Bill has ears like an elephant!

The Elephant Speaks

Your grandad's ears are nothing like mine,
(Which are sensitive, soft and uncommonly fine).
No ! Your ears, Grandad Bill, are all spotty and red –
No match for the visions that sprout from my head.
My ears are a hundred times bigger than yours –
When I'm out and about, they elicit applause.
"Oh wow !" my fans whisper. "His ears are so sleek –
So cool and refined and incredibly chic."
They look on in awe and a low rumble starts:
"Three cheers for the ears that have stolen our hearts!"

Punctuation

Beware the Exclamation Mark!
I dreamed I met one in the park.
It bellowed "Ooh!" and "Wow!" and "Whee!"
And chased me round and round a tree.
Behind it bounced a Question Mark –
It had an irritating bark. It yelped
"Why? What?" and "When?" and "Where?"
Then, flying at me through the air,
Came every type of punctuation,
Screaming "Now for your education!"
A Comma yelled "Where do we go?"
"Oh help!" I groaned. "How should I know?"

and that is when i woke up thats it ive done
with punctuation i said im never going to use
a question mark again do you blame me

That Was Then

The Song of the Dodo

Imagine him upon the sandy shore –
The lonely dodo, gazing out to sea.
What was his cry? A croak? A caw?
Surely a creature so preposterous –
With tufted tail, ungainly bulk,
Small wasted wings and monstrous beak,
Would stretch upon his stubby toes
And screech, or squawk, or shriek?

It may be, though, that he was compensated
For his odd face, the way he lurched along.
Perhaps he carolled like a nightingale,
Sending pure, silver streams of song
Higher and higher, to those regions where
His own poor, flightless body
Never could aspire –
Flooding the azure air with trills,
With thrilling waterfalls of sound –
Till all the island,
All the hills around,
Lay there, entranced and still.

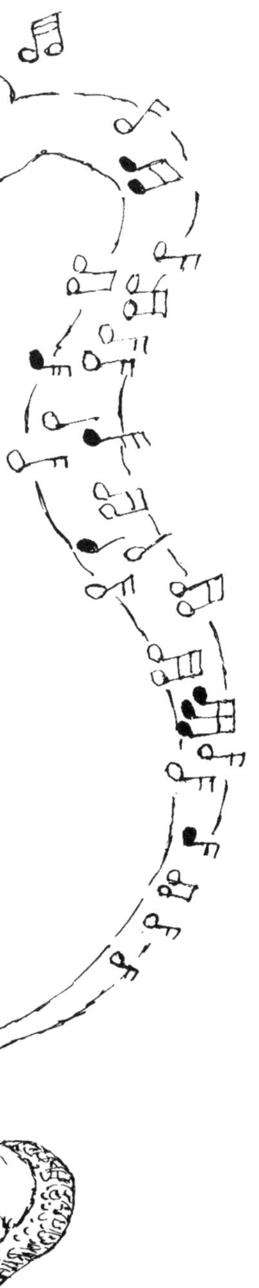

Magpies

The formal magpies,
Painted long ago,
Pattern the ceiling
Of the palace hall.

And far below,
In ornate frames,
A cavalcade
Of kings and queens
Goes marching
Through the centuries.

A proud parade,
In armour, plumes,
In farthingales,
They change
From age to age.
In curls and ruffs
And powdered wigs,
In lacey cuffs
And crinolines,
They stride their stage.

Outside, a magpie
Perches on a wall –
The very image
Of his pied relations
Who grace the ceiling
Of the painted hall.

"Picasso? Huh!"

"Picasso? Huh! Thinks he can paint?
Nobody looks like that!" says Joe.
"She's blue and made of triangles –
Her eyes don't fit! Look at her nose!"

He stamps away, but I stay put;
I think it's good – I really do;
For when I cry, I feel like that –
Scrunched up, heart-broken, blue.

Face splintered, like her handkerchief,
She hunches shoulders sharp with grief.
Her eyes explode with tears that race
Down the cold angles of her face.

When Sophie wouldn't come and play
And I fell down and hurt my knee;
When Tiff, our kitten, ran away –
I felt like that. She feels like me.

Upon her head's a scarlet hat,
A blue flower glowing at its brim.
(She must have put it on before
The bad thing happened
And the world went dim).
Perhaps she fell, or lost her cat . . .

Or was it something worse than that?

ABCDEFGHIJKL

MNOPQRSTUVWXYZ

1 2 3 4 5 6 7 8 9 10

Hannah Henderson Aged 8

1784

A sampler: 1784

She signed her name in stitches:
"Hannah Henderson, aged eight."
Embroidered flowers and strawberries
And silken vines surround the date.

Look what she sewed! The alphabet
And all her numbers, in a line;
And birds and cats and grazing cows –
I couldn't do that – and I'm nine!

She sewed a house, shaped like a box,
A horse with horns, a dog, a fox,
Some faded trees like lollipops
And ladies in old-fashioned frocks.

I wonder if she sewed her thoughts
Into that deer? That wonky gate?
That butterfly? But all I know
Is "Hannah Henderson, aged eight."

To the Namers

Tyrannosaurus, Stegosaurus,
Sauropod and Theropod,
Brontosaurus, Diplodocus –
That is how you branded us.

Listen! Once we were known
By our roars and our tread;
By our shimmering scales;
Creaking wings overhead.

We left long ago,
Scattering clues –
Sealed in the silting sand,
The muddy ooze.
Locked in the living rock,
Concealed from view,
In amber and in coal,
We lay waiting for you.

Name us, then, decipher us –
Pterodactyl, Placodus.

You think you know us?
No! You'll never know
Our creaks, our roars,
Our dazzling hues –
The way we shook
The forest floor.

An Old Photo

Framed in red plush and sepia-tinted,
Her mouth about to tremble, (she looks scared),
She's poised for flight, a pale, uncertain moth;
She knows she'd rather be elsewhere.
She's posing in her starch-stiff smock
And cotton stockings, freshly on today.
Her little feet, in strappy shoes
Are neatly placed at five to two.

One hand grasps a spray of paper roses,
The other's resting lightly on a chair.
That chair! A scary, crouching monster,
Carved with dark vines and gargoyle grins,
It looms above her; cuts her down to size –
A glowering presence, towering, waiting there.

And afterwards? Released into her present,
Did she escape and cry? Maybe.
Or did she roll about the lawn,
Muddy her dress and rumple up her hair?
Shout at her brothers, scream with laughter,
Fly to her future – and forget the chair?

My First Fossil

In a dazzle of sunlight,
The stone split apart;
It fell neatly in two,
As sweet as a peach.

But in place of a kernel,
In each of its halves,
There nestled a shell –
Two halves of a whole;
Two perfect impressions,
One curving outward,
The other a hollow,
Half the size of my nail.

They lay in my palm,
Not two shells, but one;
A shell lit by the sun –
The same sun that blazed
Countless ages ago
On the warm, shallow bed
Of the sea.

This is Now

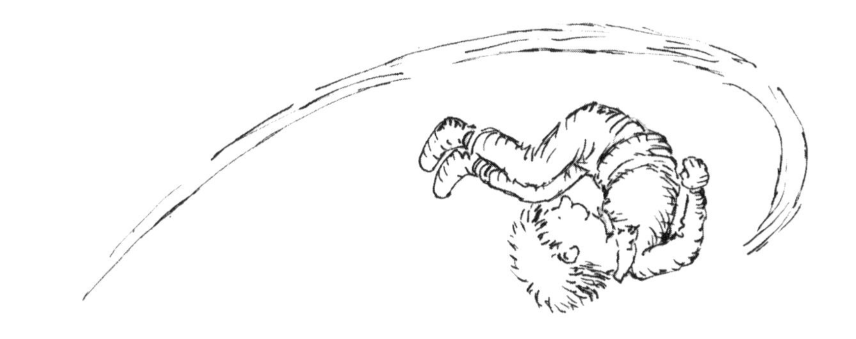

Upside Down

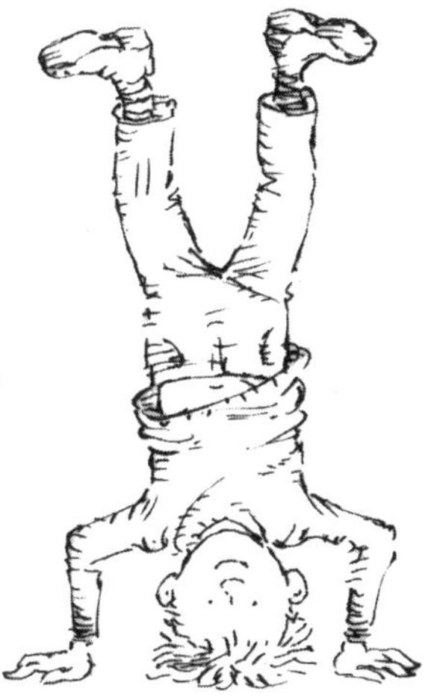

I learned to do head-over-heels
Then how to stand upon my head;
And next I balanced on my hands
And walked around like that instead.

I walk like this around the house,
I walk like this around the town.
I won't turn up the other way –
Life's more exciting upside down.

Snake

Ss!
Ss!
Silver
Sliver
Grass
Shiver-
Slither,
Slide,
Golden-
Eyed.
Ssss!
Glide
Through
Pearled
Dew-
Field
Edges,
Ponds,
Hedges.
Ssss!
Swim,
Skim
Pond's
Rim;
Twine,
Wind,
Stream-
Lined.
Sssss!
Coil,
Curl,
Swirl,
Unfurl;
Bask,
Laze,
Spark,
Blaze.
Slow,
Shy,
Swift,
Sly.
Sss!
Ss!
S!

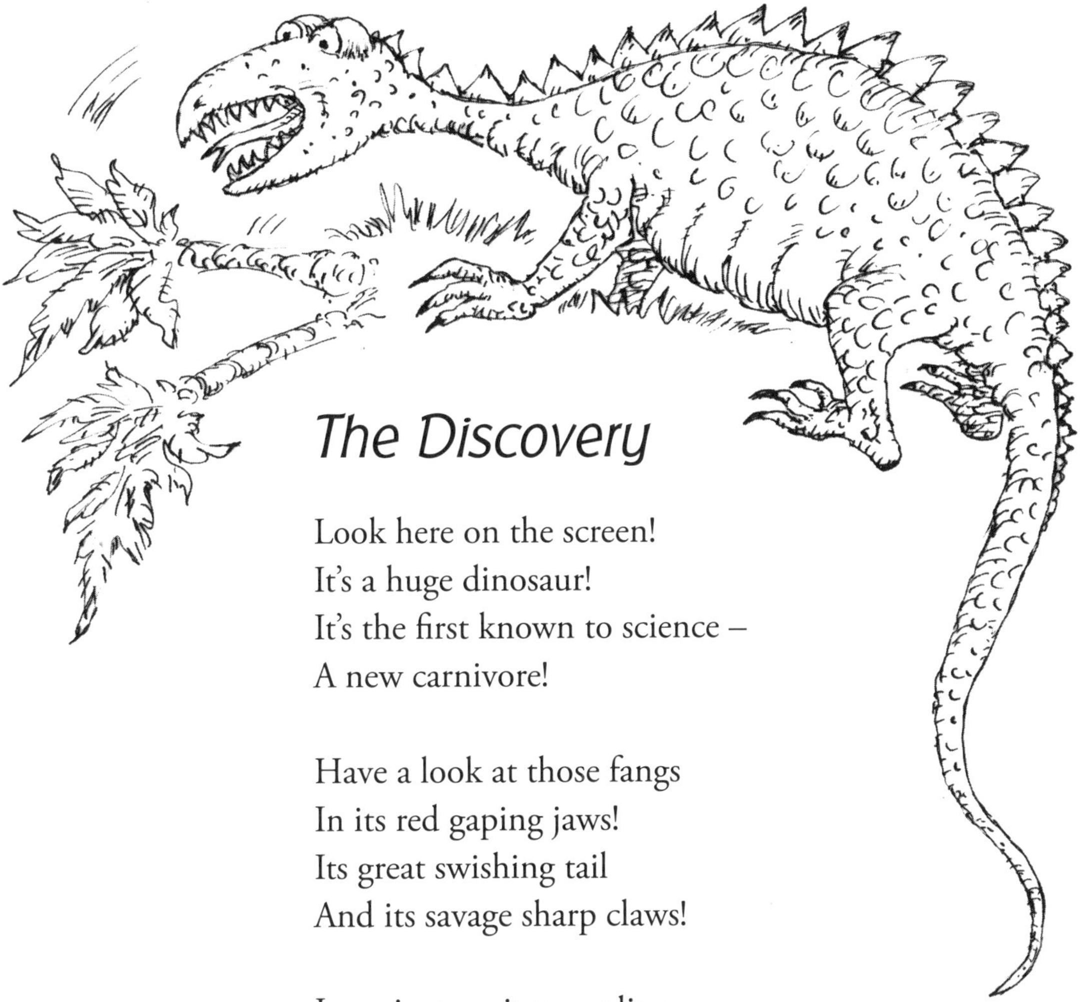

The Discovery

Look here on the screen!
It's a huge dinosaur!
It's the first known to science –
A new carnivore!

Have a look at those fangs
In its red gaping jaws!
Its great swishing tail
And its savage sharp claws!

I can just see it trampling
The dark forest floor,
Flattening trees,
Shattering earth with its roar!

Hang on! What's it say?
I don't understand.
"It was the size of a mouse –
It could sit in your hand."

The Graphene Exhibition

This graphene is magic!
It's in all sorts of things –
Like filters and light bulbs
And aeroplane wings.

Two scientists found it –
They were messing about
With sticky tape and black lead
When one gave a shout –

"Eureka! We've cracked it!
Do you know what this means?
Just look at these specks!
We've located graphene!"

Over there on the wall
There's a face on the screen;
Mr Sissay's reciting
His ode to graphene.

And now we're invited
To post notes on a board,
With ideas for graphene –
"I know!" yells Matt Lord.

"I'd make a machine
To demolish the school."
"No! Try again, Matthew!"
Glares Mrs McCall.

But I am inspired!
I'll do science one day –
Or perhaps be a poet
Like Mr Sissay.

Pizza, Mr Caesar?

I dreamed up a party –
At first it seemed fun.
I asked Julius Caesar
And Attila the Hun.
I invited a Viking,
Called Erik the Red.
Then I asked Robin Hood
And I put on a spread.

As I passed the food round
I bowed and I said
"Mr Caesar – some pizza?
Gingerbread, Mr Red?
Treacle pud, Mr Hood?
Cream bun, Mr Hun?
Some custard? Some gravy?
Tomato sauce, anyone?"

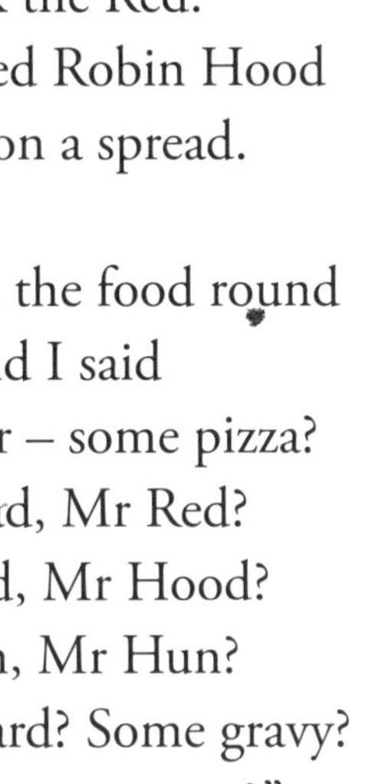

But it was a disaster!
They hated each other;
The place was in chaos
Till in came my mother.
She soon cleared the room;
She banged a brass gong,
Yelling

Get back to history –
Where you belong!
And please get that chariot
Off my front lawn!

They melted away
And were lost in the dawn.
I woke with a start
As I heard myself scream –
"There! There!" said my mum.
"It was only a dream."

Too Many Torcs

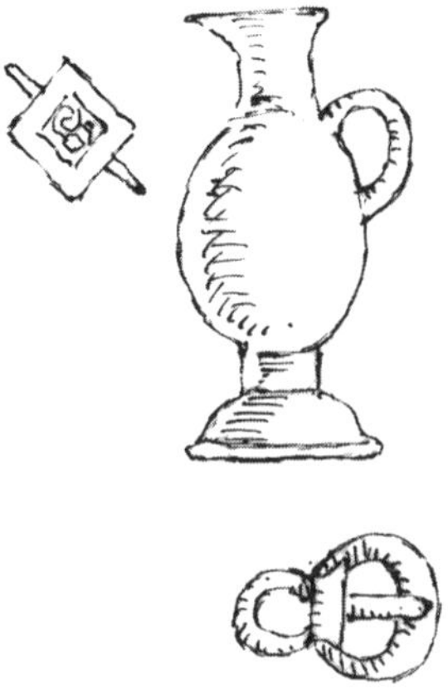

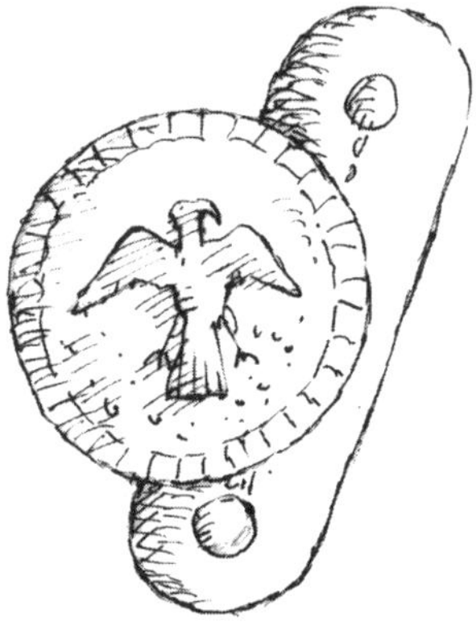

It's a good exhibition!
But – please, Mr York –
Why was it those Celts
Had so many torcs?

There are anklets and axes
And flagons and ladles,
Mirrors and cauldrons
And goblets and cradles.

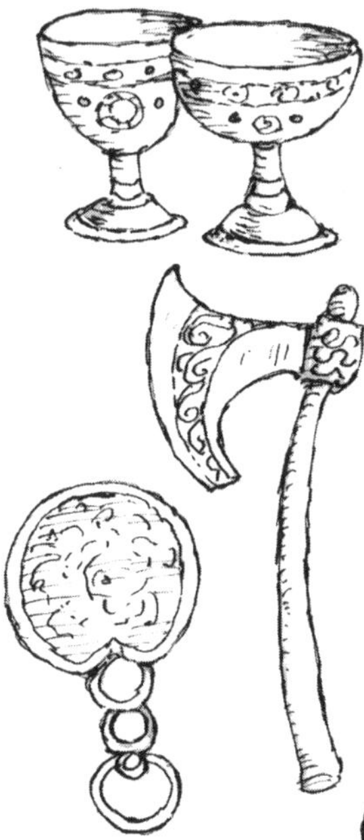

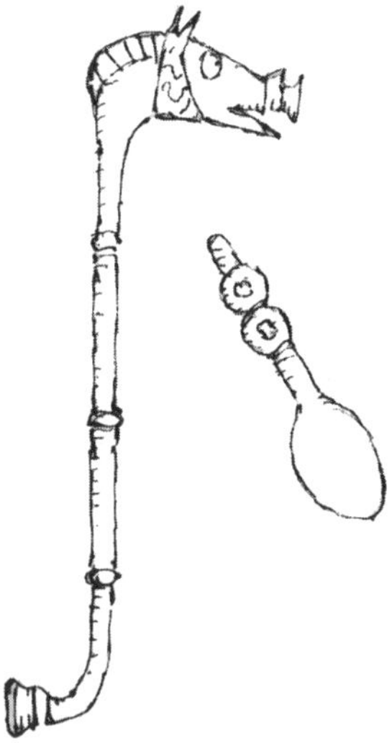

A torc

A Celt →

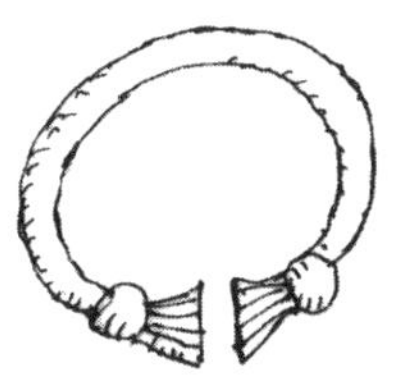
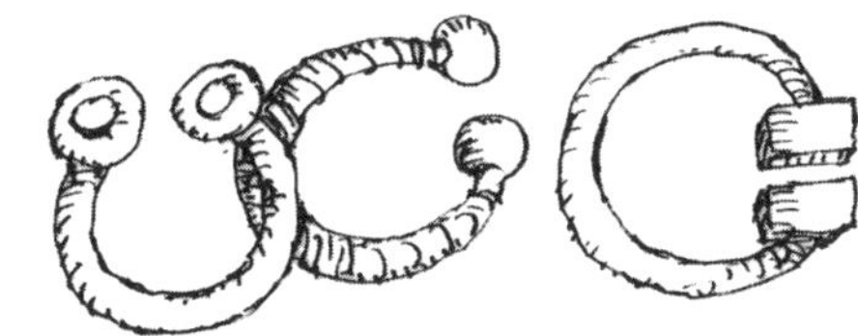
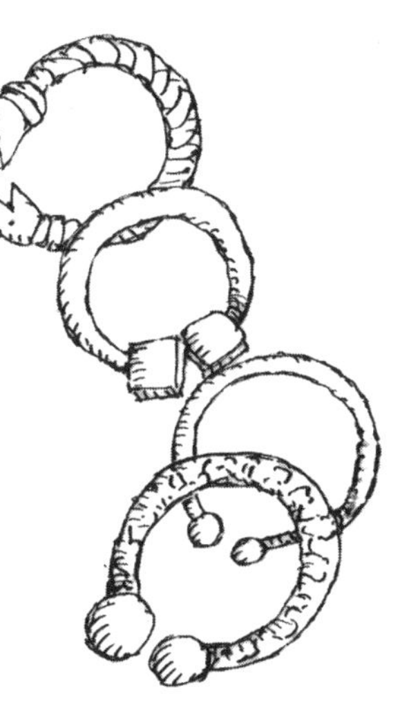

I like the big shields
Decorated with hawks,
But I can't say I'm keen
On the great piles of torcs.

I like brooches and buckles –
And trumpets, of course –
And the helmet with horns
That was made for a horse.

But if you ask me,
It's all wrong, Mr York –
They've gone over the top –
There are too many torcs!

Starling

He settles, stretches,
Flaps his wings;
Rests for a while,
Then turns his head,
To check that he's alone.
And now his morning song begins –
Low clucks and whistles,
Screeches and soft croons.
And all the while,
As backing to the track,
His beak clacks out
A rhythm of its own.
His feathered collar
Blazes with blue fire;
It rises, falls,
With every freckled phrase.

Tonight, before the sun has set,
He'll join the ghostly gathering
That streams across the sky.
He'll sink into the teeming crowd –
A single pixel, part of the great swarm
That wheels and whirls and changes shape,
With just one will, one mind.

But as for now,
He stands alone;
Shimmers in sunlight,
Quivers in the breeze;
Throws back his head
And screams with joy .

The Hayfield

We left it standing –
A vast, forbidden territory.
Only the foxes
And the field-mice
Sneaked and scurried there
Amongst the nodding grass
And all the flowers
Of summer.

As we walked home,
We sensed it in the air –
The sweet sap smell
Came drifting, long before
We saw the flattened rows.
We yelled and ran,
Eager to own the silver field –
Our new and shining kingdom.

Cloudland

The Day I Flew

The day I flew
I spread my wings
And rose upon
A warm west wind.

I soared with birds!
I flew so high
I chased the sun
Across the sky.

At night I traced
The Milky Way;
How far I flew
I couldn't say.

I miss my wings;
I miss the sky,
Now I've forgotten
How to fly.

Elsewhere

She was lost in a book.
She'd opened it up
And stepped through a door,
Straight into a forest –
A forest of whispering leaves.
She met a new friend there;
They dodged dragons and demons,
Fought an army of trolls,
Slept fast under stars
And sailed shining streams.
At last the giant's castle
Was looming above them –

a voice called.

And she was hauled back
In the wink of an eye –
Past streams and past stars,
Trolls, demons and dragons,
Past her friend, past the trees.
And BANG! went the door;
And there she was, home –
Back home where she'd started.

And the world had turned grey;
Much like before.

The Road is a River

Sometimes I think
That the road is a river;
I follow the tide
As it flows through the town.
The shops and the houses
Melt into a mist;
Cars become crocodiles,
Traffic lights drown.
Palm trees are swaying –
They dip to the water;
A flock of flamingoes
Goes wading on by.
I paddle in shallows,
Fish nibble my ankles;
A cloud of white butterflies
Floats in the sky.
Parakeets screech
And blossoms are falling;
I brush through the rushes
That tickle my knees.
Dragonflies hover
On ruffles and ripples –
The sweet smell of cinnamon
Drifts on the breeze.

By a bend in the river,
Moored fast to a willow,
A blue boat is waiting –
It's waiting for me.

So now I am floating
And dreaming and floating –
To the blue river mouth
And the wide open sea.

Dreams

Sophie and her sister Claire
Built a castle in the air;
Filled it up with dreams and hopes –
With bicycles and skipping ropes,
A skating rink, a swimming pool –
"Hurray!" said Claire. "Goodbye to school!"

But look out, Sophie! Look out Claire!
Sailing towards you through the air
Comes little Lenny Valentine;
His team's just won – he's on Cloud Nine.
He's dreaming of the First Division –
Oh no! Look out! Mid-air collision!

The cloud dissolves, the castle slumps,
They fall to earth with two big bumps.
"Sick? As a parrot!" mutters Len;
"Come on!" says Claire. "Let's start again."

Summer

Summer smells like strawberries,
Like barbecues
And drying hay.

Summer tastes like candyfloss,
Like lemonade
And salty spray.

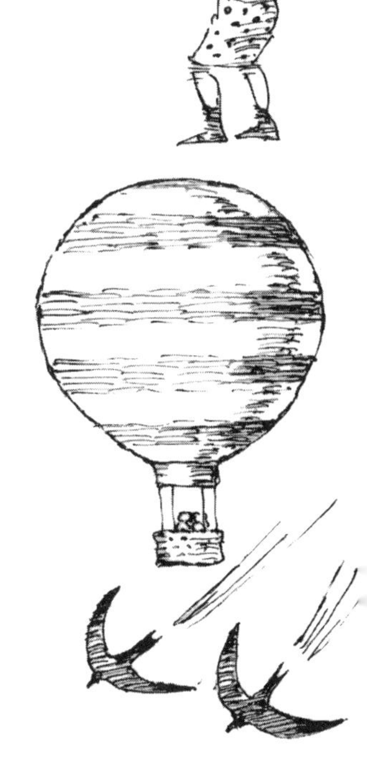

Summer looks like shooting stars,
Hot-air balloons
And blue, blue skies.

Summer sounds like screaming swifts,
Like ice-cream vans
And buzzing flies.

Summer feels like tingling waves,
Like scorching sand,
Like sun-burned knees.

And summer smells like strawberries.

Borderline

The magic time is here –
The no-man's land
Between the day and night,
When pale flowers burn
Like phosphorous
And moths fly, flickering,
In the fading light.
Cats twitch and leap
Upon the dew-damp lawn
And barn-owls haunt the hedges,
Drifting, silent, white.

And now I'm free!
Weightless, I skim the grass.
I'm running, running –
Faster than I've ever run before.
I'm moon-struck! Light!
One toe-touch and I leap,
I soar; no longer bound to earth,
I melt into the borderline
Between the half-light
And the half-dark shore.

Rabbits

The sea is deep blue,
And freckled with shadows.
The sun scores a path
From horizon to shore.
Sea-thrift and thyme
Embroider the cliff-top
And high, high above,
The herring-gulls soar.

From the top of the bus,
We can just see the rabbits –
Small tiger-skin rugs,
Splayed out on the turf –
Cocooned by the heat
And ignoring the traffic,
The cries of the seabirds,
The roar of the surf.

Words

They start to grow –
At first, a tiny pebble;
Then half-formed charms,
Strung on a broken chain.
Finally, a dazzle
Of bright beads,
Some intricate, some plain,
Linked by a silver strand.

Words:
Buzzing, bruising,
Whispering, wounding,
Sinking, singing,
Sidling through the brain.

Guardians of hoards;
Sharp as the stinging rain,
And swift as arrows
Greedy for their goal.
Flights of fancy;
Freedom chimes.

Words:
Treasure-laden argosies;
Travellers in time.

More poetry to enjoy by Hilda Offen

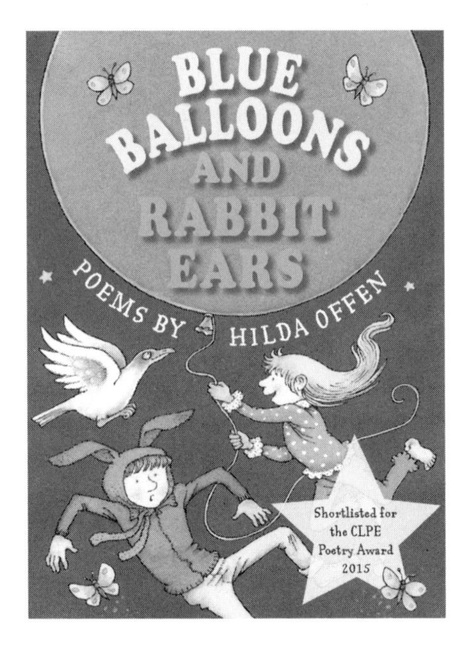

Blue Balloons and Rabbit Ears

Shortlisted for the CLiPPA Poetry Award

'An appealing collection for young children, illustrated by the poet. Full of fun and rhyme and rhythm and a variety of verse forms, it includes thoughtful themes about nature and history too.' – **CLiPPA judges**

'An enticing mix of original nursery rhymes and poems to entertain all ages.' – **Parents in Touch**

'The playful title perfectly captures the spirit of this delightful collection. Readily accessible through their strong adherence to rhythm and rhyme, the poems' subject matter will appeal to a wide age range ... a collection which children can return to for many years.' – **Carousel**

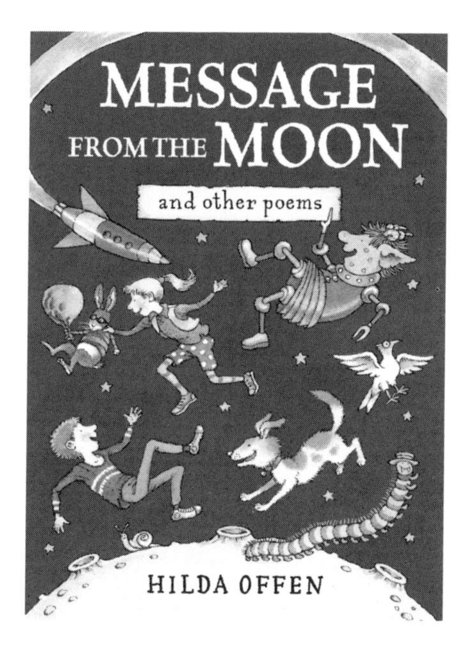

Message from the Moon

Selected for The Reading Agency 2017 Summer Reading Challenge

'Inviting poems celebrate the wonder, variety and possibility of a young child's world' – **Books for Keeps**

'There is a romp and a rhyme for everyone in this delicious mix of imaginative, thoughtful and funny poems' – **Lancashire Evening Post**

'Dazzling and inventive pieces'– **The Bookbag**